CW00420581

A Romantic Sketchbook for Piano

BOOK I

50 easy pieces composed *c.*1830 – *c.*1950

The pieces in this album, of about Grades 1–2 in standard,
have been selected to provide a variety of tempi, styles and moods.

Original source material has been followed, but obvious errors and
minor inconsistencies in phrasing and dynamics have been corrected
without specific comment. Editorial suggestions for pedalling and
for metronome marks are shown within square brackets but should
not be considered in any way authoritative. Other editorial matters
are mentioned in the footnotes to the pieces.

The titles of pieces and works in this album are given in
English, either original or in translation.

Alan Jones

The Associated Board of
the Royal Schools of Music

Contents

Handwritten margin notes:

♩ = 1 beat

♫) ♪ = ½ beat

♪ = ¼ beat

♬ = 1 beat

(½ ¼ ¼)

♩♪♪ = 1 beat

p = soft

f = loud

cresc. = getting louder

𝄆 : :𝄇 = repeat

mf = medium loud

mp = u soft

⟍ = getting louder

⟋ = getting softer

➤✳︎◄

STUDY in C

MAYER, Op.340 No.1

Born in Prussia to a clarinettist father and a piano teacher mother, Charles Mayer (1799–1862) was taken as a baby with his family to Russia, where he later studied the piano with Field. He taught in St Petersburg for 30 years, as well as touring throughout Europe giving piano recitals, and then settled in Dresden for the last decade of his life. He composed a vast number of piano works, mainly for teaching purposes.

© 1996 by The Associated Board of the Royal Schools of Music   AB 2344

LESSON in C

DIABELLI, Op.125 No.7

Remembered today for writing the waltz commission for Beethoven's 33 piano variations under his name, Anton Diabelli (1781–1858) was born near Salzburg and studied music at an early age. For a time he taught the piano and guitar in Vienna before joining a music publishing firm, which he managed from 1824 to 1852 and which published most of Schubert's works. His own compositions include sacred and chamber music, works for the guitar and instructive piano pieces.

LESSON in F

BRUNNER, Op.487 No.38

LESSON in D

BRUNNER, Op.487 No.41

Andantino [♩ = c.112]

A German organist and conductor of choral societies, Christian Brunner (1792–1874) was born in Saxony. His output as a composer amounted to over 500 opus numbers, including many transcriptions and arrangements of well-known melodies for the domestic pianist and lots of easy piano pieces for children.

STUDY in D

CZERNY, Op.187 No.49

The Viennese-born Karl Czerny (1791–1857) learned the piano from his father and had become so proficient by the age of nine that Beethoven agreed to instruct him. Profiting also from his acquaintance with Hummel and Clementi, he started to teach at the age of 15, Liszt being one of his most talented pupils. He was a prolific composer in all spheres of music, but today his fame rests upon his many piano studies. In this one, the slurs have been slightly revised and the dynamics amplified.

PASTORALE

J. F. BURGMÜLLER, Op.100 No.3

Born in Bavaria, Johann Friedrich Burgmüller (1806–1874) belonged to a musical family, his younger brother Norbert being a gifted composer who died at an early age. As a young man, Friedrich settled in Paris where he became a popular pianist, improvising hundreds of salon pieces and composing many works for the amateur player. Today he is only remembered by teachers and students for his Op.100 & 109 studies. In this one, the slurs have been revised to cross bar-lines.

STUDY in F

Mouvement de Valse [♩ = c.144]

J.-B. DUVERNOY, Op.176 No.17

D.C. al Fine

A member of a large and distinguished family of French musicians, some of whom were instrumental teachers at the Paris Conservatoire, Jean-Baptiste Duvernoy (1800–1880) was born and studied in Paris, where he became a well-known teacher of the piano. He composed many transcriptions and arrangements for the piano as well as divertissements, fantasies, rondos, airs, mazurkas and technical studies.

AB 2344

THE WILD HORSEMAN

SCHUMANN, Op.68 No.8

One of the foremost German composers of the Romantic era, Robert Schumann (1810–1856) was born at Zwickau in Saxony. His considerable output includes four symphonies, three concertos, about 100 choral works, chamber music, over 300 songs and much piano music. This piece comes from his *Album for the Young*, which he composed in Dresden in 1848 with his young family around him. He wrote: 'I don't remember ever having been in such good form .... The pieces simply poured out one after another.'

MELODY

Arabian Air

LE COUPPEY, *ABC du Piano* No.28

A Parisian by birth, Félix Le Couppey (1811–1887) studied at the Conservatoire, where he was appointed an assistant teacher of harmony at the early age of 17. He continued to teach there for nearly 60 years, specialising in the piano for the final 30 years. In this capacity he composed numerous studies for his instrument as well as an extensive tutorial course.

DEDICATION

Molto lentamente, con espressione, ♩ = 44

HELLER, Op.138 No.1

Born in Hungary near Pest, Stephen Heller (1813–1888) was a child prodigy pianist and toured Europe until he suffered a nervous breakdown. In due course he settled in Paris, where he tried to earn a living as a pianist, critic and composer; but, although befriended by Berlioz, Chopin and Liszt, his life was largely one of loneliness and poverty. All trace of his larger-scale works has been lost, but his short piano pieces continue to remain popular today. In this one, the grace notes in bb.5 & 14 have been written out, and the bracketed notes may be omitted.

STUDY in C

LOESCHHORN, Op.65 No.3

STUDY in G

LOESCHHORN, Op.65 No.9

Albert Loeschhorn (1819–1905) was born in Berlin and studied at the city's Royal Institute for Church Music. He later taught the piano there, being given the title of Royal Professor, and was highly regarded as a teacher by many talented pupils. He also organised and took part in regular chamber music concerts. Although he composed many works, he is known today only for the instructive studies he wrote for the piano. In these two melodic examples, the dynamics are editorial.

AB 2344

STUDY in C

GURLITT, Op.50 No.3

Moderato [♩ = c.116]

SERENADE

GURLITT, Op.140 No.18

Andantino con moto [♩. = c.88]

Born into an artistic family in Altona when it was part of Denmark, Cornelius Gurlitt (1820–1901), a pupil of Reinecke's father, began his career as organist at the city's Cathedral. He later taught in Copenhagen and then became a professor at the Hamburg Conservatory. Greatly influenced by Schumann, to whom he paid a special visit, he composed a variety of works but today is known only for an immense number of piano pieces, written largely for teaching purposes.

ON THE PLAYGROUND

KÖHLER, Op.210 No.5

Louis Köhler (1820–1886) was born in Brunswick and studied there and in Vienna. After holding posts as a theatre conductor, he settled in Königsberg (Kaliningrad), where he remained for the rest of his life and where he established a piano school. Apart from composing three operas, a ballet and a symphony, he produced a large output of educational piano music, and he also contributed regular articles to music periodicals. The piece comes from his *Children's Album*.

PIANO PIECE FOR THE YOUNG
No.13

H. HENKEL

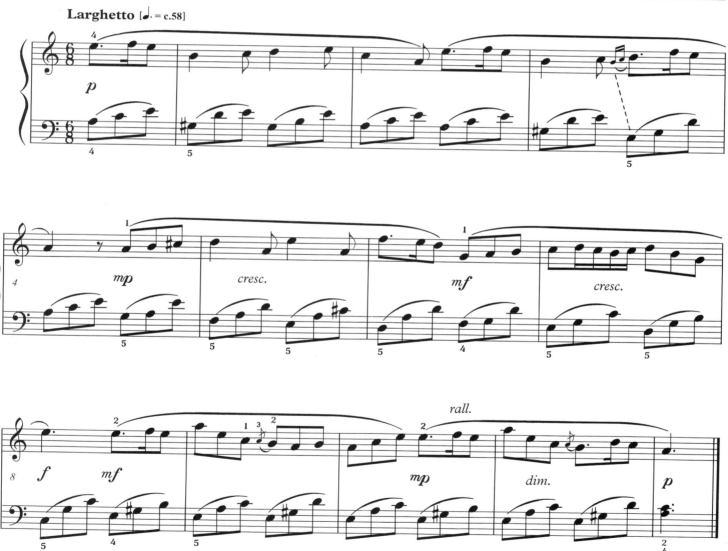

Heinrich Henkel (1822–1899) was born in Fulda and studied the piano with his father and with Aloys Schmitt. At the age of 27 he settled in Frankfurt, where he earned a living as a teacher and composer, publishing a tutorial method for the piano and writing many songs and piano pieces. The r.h. phrase marks in this piece are editorial as are the dynamics.

NEW SCENE FROM CHILDHOOD

T. F. KIRCHNER, Op.55 No.4

Born near Chemnitz, Theodor Kirchner (1823–1903) studied in Leipzig, where he made the acquaintance of Schumann and Mendelssohn. On the latter's recommendation, he obtained the post of organist at Winterthur in Switzerland and remained there for 20 years before moving to Zurich, where he was active as a conductor. Subsequently he taught in Würzburg, Leipzig, Dresden and Hamburg. He composed about 90 piano works, this piece coming from an album written in the manner of Schumann's *Scenes from Childhood*.

AB 2344

SIMPLICITY

REINECKE, Op.254 No.10

A friend of Gurlitt, also born in Altona, Carl Reinecke (1824–1910) was a proficient player of the violin and the piano, and first played in public at the age of 11. In 1844 he was appointed court pianist in Copenhagen and made a number of concert tours, performing in London on several occasions. Later, for 35 years he was conductor of the Gewandhaus in Leipzig, where he was also professor of composition at the Conservatory. A prolific composer, he wrote mainly for the piano, most of his output being of an instructional nature.

AB 2344

TO BEGIN WITH

WILM, Op.81 No.1

Born in Riga, Nicolai von Wilm (1834–1911) studied at the Leipzig Conservatory and then returned to his native city as a theatre conductor. He later taught in St Petersburg before settling first in Dresden and then in Wiesbaden. He composed mainly chamber and instrumental works, including a great deal of piano music. This piece is the first item in an album of *Little Pieces*.

AB 2344

THE INDUSTRIOUS STUDENT

K. J. BISCHOFF, Op. 31 No. 3

Kaspar Bischoff (1823–1893) was born in Ansbach and studied in Munich and Leipzig. He then settled in Frankfurt where he taught singing and founded a choral society. Apart from an opera, three symphonies, some chamber works and church music, he composed a number of piano pieces. In this one, from an album of easy pieces he wrote for his young daughter's instruction, the dynamics are editorial.

CUCKOO

BRESLAUR, Op.46 No.21

WATER MUSIC

BRESLAUR, Op.46 No.10

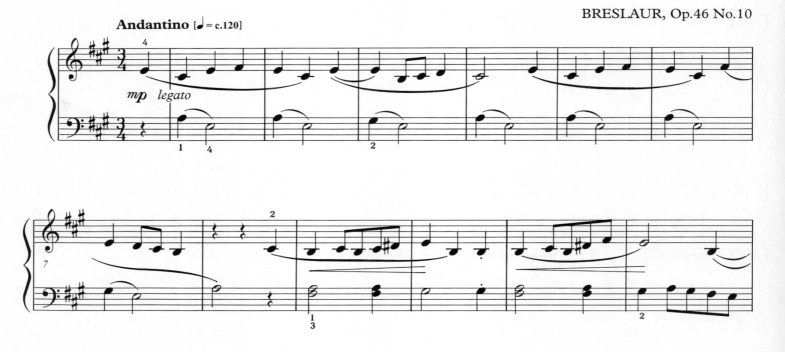

WALTZ

BRESLAUR, Op.46 No.25

Emil Breslaur (1836–1899) was born in Kottbus and studied in Berlin, where he later taught at Kullak's Academy and was choirmaster at the Reformed Synagogue. He founded a teachers' association and also edited a periodical on music education. He was the author of a number of books on piano technique and composed many pieces for the instrument. In these three easy examples, the dynamics are editorial.

CHILD'S SONG

GUILMANT, Op.48 No.1

Félix Guilmant (1837–1911) became a church organist in his native town of Boulogne at the age of 15. He later moved to Paris, where he was organist at the Trinité for 30 years and where he taught at the Conservatoire. He made numerous recital tours of Europe and America, thereby establishing a considerable reputation in the musical world. He composed much music for the organ but little for the piano. This piece is the first in an album of six pieces possibly intended for his daughter's instruction.

AB 2344

SCHERZINO

E. HORÁK, *Kinder-Klavierschule* No.112

Born in Bohemia, Eduard Horák (1838–1892) settled in Vienna where, with his brother Adolf, he founded the Horák Pianoforte School, which quickly gained a notable reputation throughout Europe. The two of them wrote a large number of teaching pieces for their pupils and were the authors of a practical manual, from which this piece, aptly meaning 'a little joke', comes.

AB 2344

'GO TO SLEEP'

SANDRÉ

The French composer and teacher, Gustave Sandré (1843–1916) was for many years a professor at the Nancy Conservatoire. He wrote songs, chamber music and many piano pieces, some of which were regularly published as supplements to the magazine *L'Illustration*, including an album *For the little ones*, from which this piece about a girl rocking her doll comes.

SAD AT HEART

Etwas bewegt [Con moto, ♩ = c.116]

FUCHS, Op.47 No.5

Born in the Styria (Steiermark) district of Austria, Robert Fuchs (1847–1927) started to study various instruments at an early age. When he was 18, he settled in Vienna to earn a living as an organist, répétiteur and teacher. At the same time he continued his studies at the Conservatory, where he later taught a generation of musicians who included Mahler, Sibelius and Wolf. He composed orchestral, choral and chamber works as well as much piano music. This piece comes from an *Album for the Young*.

STUDY in D

M. VOGEL, Op.34 Part II No.4

Moritz Vogel (1846–1922) was born in Silesia and studied in Leipzig, where he later worked as a teacher. He also conducted choral societies, wrote music criticism and was the author of a history of music. His compositions include choral and organ works, songs and a methodical series of instructional piano pieces. In this study, all the slurs and dynamics, apart from the hairpins, are editorial.

ROUNDELAY

Einfach [Semplice, ♩ = c.112]

A. FÖRSTER, Op.39 No.2

The German violinist, Alban Förster (1849–1916), was born in Reichenbach and studied at the Dresden Conservatory, where later he was to teach. He also held court musical posts at Neustrelitz where he died. His compositions include a ballet, orchestral and chamber works, violin music, songs and educational piano pieces. This piece comes from an *Album for the Young*.

WHO IS THERE?

SARTORIO, Op.783 No.9

TWO FROGS

SARTORIO, Op.783 No.12

Of Italian descent, Arnoldo Sartorio (1853–?) was born in Frankfurt, studied there and later became a teacher. He also held conducting posts and directed choral societies in Strasbourg, Düsseldorf and Cologne. He is credited with composing over 1,000 opus numbers, most of which are works for the piano. These three pieces come from an album of *Youthful Recreations*.

ON TIP-TOE

SARTORIO, Op.783 No.8

CATCH BALL

MATTHAY, Op.35 Book I No.3

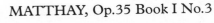

Of German parentage, the piano teacher, Tobias Matthay (1858–1945), was born in London and studied under Sterndale Bennett and Sullivan at the Royal Academy of Music, where he was later to be a professor for 50 years. He was the author of a number of books on his theories of piano technique and teaching methods, and he founded a school to propagate his ideas, numbering many distinguished performers among his pupils. He composed 46 works, including some songs and much piano music.

Copyright 1925 by Tobias Matthay. Reproduced by permission of Oxford University Press.

AB2344

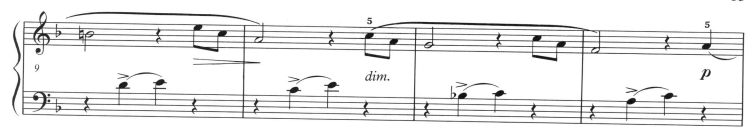

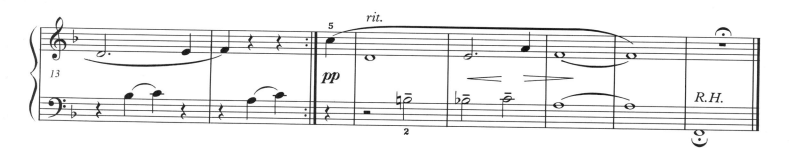

THE ECHO

Molto allegro e legatissimo [♩. = c.108]

ALBANESI

Carlo Albanesi (1856–1926) was born in Naples and learned the piano with his father. After touring Italy and France giving recitals, he settled permanently in England at the age of 26. Ten years later he was appointed to a professorship of piano at the Royal Academy of Music, and he also became an examiner for the Associated Board. His compositions include a few chamber works, some songs, six piano sonatas and other piano pieces.

A JOLLY MOMENT

LADUKHIN

Nikolai Ladukhin (1860–1918) was born in St Petersburg and studied at the Moscow Conservatory, where later he was to become a professor, Gedike being one of his many pupils. He wrote several textbooks on harmony and composed a few orchestral, choral and chamber works, as well as songs and piano pieces for children.

FAREWELL

Andantino [♩ = c.108]

GRECHANINOV, Op.98 No.4

Alexander Grechaninov (1864–1956) was born in Moscow and studied under Arensky at its Conservatory and under Rimsky-Korsakov at the St Petersburg Conservatory. He spent the first 60 years of his life mostly in Moscow, then settled in Paris and later moved to New York, where he became an American citizen. He composed a number of orchestral and chamber works, but today he is best known for his liturgical works and his piano music for children.

WANDERING

P. ZILCHER, Op.109 No.1

Born in Frankfurt, Paul Zilcher (1855–1943) learned the piano with his father and taught his own son Hermann, who became a well-known teacher and composer in Germany. Besides founding the Parlow-Zilcher Piano School in Offenbach (Main), he composed a great number of piano and instrumental pieces for teaching purposes.

AB 2344

CHINESE STATUETTE

REBIKOV, *Christmas Gifts* No.13

Vladimir Rebikov (1866–1920) was born in Siberia and studied music in various cities. He resided for periods in Kiev, Odessa, Kishinev, Berlin, Vienna and Moscow, and died at Yalta. He was a noted writer on music, particularly on opera of which he himself composed ten works, but he is best known for his many short impressionistic piano solos, written first under the influence of Tchaikovsky but later turning against Romanticism as he experimented with the whole-tone scale.

TIRESOME PRANK

No.3

SATIE

Of French-Scots parentage, Erik Satie (1866–1925) was born in Honfleur and studied at the Paris Conservatoire without achieving much success. Afterwards he earned his living as a café pianist in Montmartre, performing some of his own songs and waltzes. At the age of 32 he retired to a suburb where he chose to live in poverty, although continuing to compose instrumental pieces and a few orchestral works. This piano piece is one of several he wrote to make full and basic use of the five fingers of each hand.

AB 2344

PIANO PIECE FOR YOUNG AND OLD

NIELSEN, Op. 53 No. 1

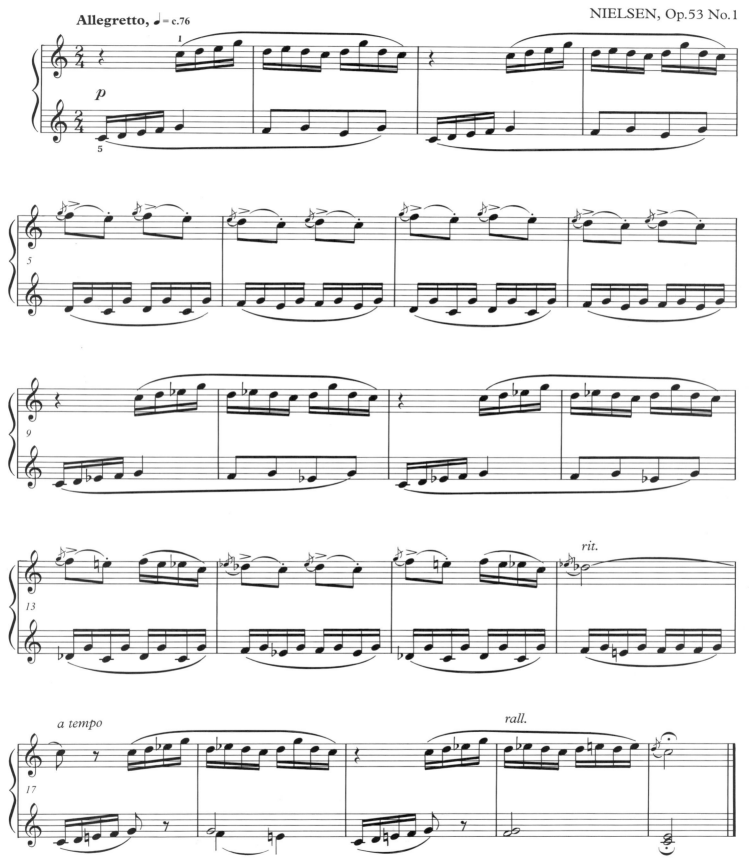

Carl Nielsen (1865–1931) was the seventh of 12 children who grew up in humble circumstances in a Danish village. He learned the violin at an early age, joined a military band in his teens and, after studying at the Copenhagen Conservatory, played in the orchestra of the Royal Chapel. He later established himself in the musical life of the city as a conductor, teacher and composer. Best known for his orchestral works, he wrote a few piano pieces. This one, like the Satie piece opposite, is based on the five fingers of each hand.

Copyright 1930 by Skandinavisk og Borups Musikforlag. Reprinted by permission of Edition Wilhelm Hansen.

AB 2344

PLAINTIVE WALTZ

SOMERVELL

Born in Windermere, Sir Arthur Somervell (1863–1937) studied composition under Stanford at Cambridge University, in Berlin and at the Royal College of Music, where later he was to teach. Although he composed a few orchestral works, his reputation today rests largely upon five song cycles. He took a great interest in music education, being a school inspector for many years, and wrote six operettas and many piano pieces for children. This one comes from an album of *Holiday Pictures*.

Copyright 1920 by Joseph Williams Ltd. Reprinted by permission of Stainer & Bell Ltd.

AB 2344

A QUIET MORNING

MAIKAPAR

Samuil Maikapar (1867–1938) was born in the Ukraine. After graduating from law school, he attended the St Petersburg Conservatory and then studied the piano with Leschetizky in Vienna. From 1910 to 1930 he was professor of piano at the St Petersburg Conservatory. His compositions are almost entirely for the piano, the most successful being in miniature form and written for children. The pedalling in this piece is editorial.

ON REFLECTION

GEDIKE, Op. 36 No. 12

Of German descent, Alexander Gedike (1877–1957) was born in Moscow into a musical family. He studied under Arensky and Ladukhin at the Moscow Conservatory and was appointed professor of piano there at the age of 26, later teaching chamber music and the organ as well. He appeared in Russia and abroad as a concert pianist and was also a notable organist. He composed four operas, four concertos and three symphonies as well as much piano music.

LULLABY

GEDIKE, Op.36 No.15

STUDY in G

DUNHILL, Op. 74 Book I No. 6

Thomas Dunhill (1877–1946) was born in London and studied composition under Stanford at the Royal College of Music, where he was to become a professor after teaching for ten years at Eton College. He first made his name as a composer of chamber music and later turned his attention to the orchestra with music for two ballets and some light operas. His educational output, particularly for the piano, was extensive, this study coming from his graded series *The Wheel of Progress*.

Copyright 1931 by The Associated Board of the Royal Schools of Music

AB 2344

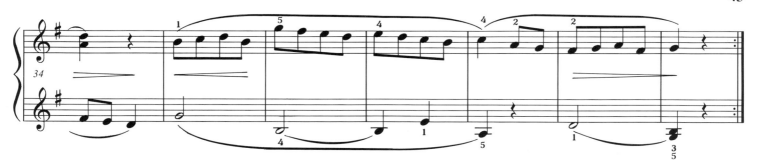

SAILOR'S SONG

SWINSTEAD

Felix Swinstead (1880–1959) was born in London and studied at the Royal Academy of Music, where later he was appointed professor of piano, a post he held for nearly 50 years. For a long time he was also an examiner of the Associated Board. His published works were numerous, mainly consisting of pieces for the piano, often written for educational purposes. This piece comes from his *Work and Play* album.

Copyright 1935 by The Associated Board of the Royal Schools of Music

A SAD TALE

KABALEVSKY, Op. 39 No. 16

Lento e poco pesante [♩ = c.92]

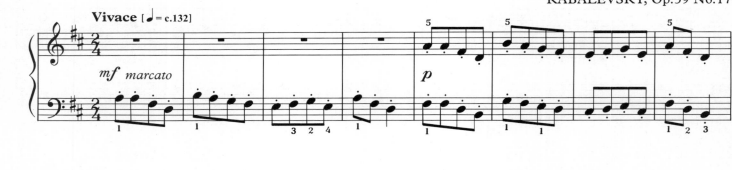

COUNTRY DANCE

KABALEVSKY, Op. 39 No. 17

Vivace [♩ = c.132]

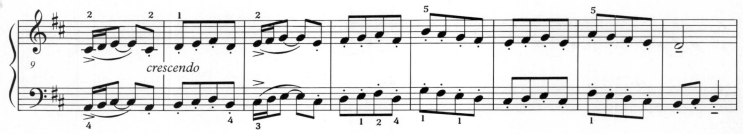

Born in St Petersburg in 1904, Dmitri Kabalevsky was able to play the piano by ear at the age of six. After deciding against a career in mathematics, he studied composition at the Moscow Conservatory where later he was to teach. His output as a composer includes six operas, four symphonies, six concertos, chamber works, and scores for ballets and films, but he is probably best known for his piano music for young children as exemplified in these three different pieces.

GALLOPING

Allegro giojoso [♩ = c.152]

KABALEVSKY, Op.39 No.15

MELODY

DYSON

Director of the Royal College of Music from 1938 to 1952, Sir George Dyson (1883–1964) was born in Halifax and studied at the R.C.M. After travelling in Italy and Germany on a Mendelssohn scholarship, he held teaching posts at various public schools (Marlborough, Rugby, Wellington and Winchester). Although he composed a number of orchestral works, he is better known for his choral music. This piano piece comes from an album of *12 Easy Pieces*.

Copyright 1952 by The Associated Board of the Royal Schools of Music

AB 2344

Processed and printed by
Halstan & Co. Ltd., Amersham, Bucks., England

12/01